C000053355

THE OFFICIAL
BRENTFORD QUIZ BOOK

THE OFFICIAL BRENTFORD QUIZ BOOK

**Compiled by Chris Cowlin
and Kevin Snelgrove**

Foreword by Peter Gilham

APEX PUBLISHING LTD

Hardback first published in 2008 by
Apex Publishing Ltd
PO Box 7086, Clacton on Sea, Essex, CO15 5WN, England
www.apexpublishing.co.uk

Copyright © 2008 by Chris Cowlin and Kevin Snelgrove
The authors have asserted their moral rights

British Library Cataloguing-in-Publication Data
A catalogue record for this book
is available from the British Library

ISBN HARDBACK: 1-906358-45-1   978-1-906358-45-7

All rights reserved. This book is sold subject to the condition, that no part of this book is to be reproduced, in any shape or form. Or by way of trade, stored in a retrieval system or transmitted in any form or by any means, electronic, mechanical, photocopying, recording, be lent, re-sold, hired out or otherwise circulated in any form of binding or cover other than that in which it is published and without a similar condition, including this condition being imposed on the subsequent purchaser, without prior permission of the copyright holder.

Typeset in 10.5pt Chianti Bdlt Win95BT

Cover Design: Siobhan Smith

Printed and bound in Great Britain by
Biddles Ltd., King's Lynn, Norfolk

Author's Note:
Please can you contact me: **ChrisCowlin@btconnect.com** if you find any mistakes/errors in this book as I would like to put them right on any future reprints of this book. I would also like to hear from Brentford fans who have enjoyed the test! For more information on me and my books please look at: **www.ChrisCowlin.com**

This book is an official product of Brentford Football Club

We would like to dedicate this book to:

All the players and staff who have worked for the club during their history.

FOREWORD

Football is our nation's favourite game. Football is everywhere, it pervades all walks of life. But however overbearing it may sometimes appear, it continues to be personal to each and every one of us Brentford Football Club is such a case, it is unique, as indeed may most clubs be to those who support them. But Brentford has a special something about it which may be difficult to describe to the lay man but is inborn in anyone who has ever been smitten by this west London club. Once bitten by these Bees there is no antidote.

Surrounded by clubs whose aspirations are being aided and abetted by untold millions, this Club continues to survive and build for the future through the simple dedication of those who are the lifeblood of the game...the supporters.

This book, through the simple use of questions and answers, will not only test your knowledge about Brentford but will also help and educate those who are not fully aware of the "who, what, when, why and how" that has shaped this great Club, and give them a better understanding of why supporting Brentford is more than just a way of life ... it is for life!

Best wishes
Peter Gilham

INTRODUCTION

I would first of all like to thank Peter Gilham for writing the foreword to this book. I am very grateful for his help on this project.

I would also like to thank all the past legends of Brentford Football Club and many current employees of the club for their comments and reviews on this book (these can be found at the back of the book).

I would also like to thank Ann Stanford and Alison Stephens for their help and advice during the books compilation.

I hope you enjoy this book. Hopefully it should bring back some wonderful memories!

It was great working with Kevin Snelgrove again, who is very well organised, between us I hope we have given you a selection of easy, medium and hard questions.

In closing, I would like to thank all my friends and family for encouraging me to complete this book.

Chris Cowlin.

Best wishes
Chris Cowlin

Visit Chris Cowlin's website:

www.ChrisCowlin.com

Visit Kevin Snelgrove's website:

www.KevinSnelgrove.co.uk

CLUB HISTORY

1. In what year was the club founded?

2. What is the name of the club's stadium?

3. What is the club's nickname?

4. Which other club helped form Brentford Football Club?

5. In what year did Brentford first play at their current stadium?

6. In 1920 Brentford was a founder member of which League?

7. In 1942 which team did Brentford beat to win the London War Cup?

8. In the late 1960s Brentford was nearly taken over by which other London club?

9. Who was the club's first ever manager from August 1900 to May 1903?

10. The club has plans for a new all-seated stadium in Lionel Road, Brentford, but what is to be the capacity?

WHO AM I? - 1

11.   I took over from Steve Perryman as Bees manager in August 1990 and left Griffin Park in May 1993.

12.   I have had three spells at the club, I am a striker who was born in March 1969, I first signed in 1989 and I scored twice on my full debut against Bolton.

13.   I made 177 League appearances for the Bees, scoring 3 goals. I made my debut in August 2000, and my nickname is Dobbo.

14.   I was born in East Ham in 1948, Brentford paid £10,000 for me in 1970 and my nickname was Twinkle Toes.

15.   I was an inside forward, born in 1925 in Southend, and I played for Southend United, Leeds, Southampton and Cardiff before signing for the Bees.

16.   I was born in Ealing in 1951 and am a legend at White Hart Lane, having made a record 655 appearances.

17.   I made 67 League appearances for the Bees, I was born in Liverpool in 1954 and my transfer fee from Colchester was £18,000.

18.   I made my debut as a 15-year-old in a League Cup tie at Watford in August 1976, I made a total of 71 League appearances for Brentford and I scored 5 goals.

19.   I signed for Brentford in 1998 from Crystal Palace for £750,000 and I was eventually sold to Wimbledon for £2.5 million.

20.   I took over from Mike Everitt as Bees manager in January 1975 and managed the club until September 1976.

CLUB RECORDS

21. The club's record League victory took place on 15 October 1963, a 9-0 win against which team?

22. How many Division Four League goals did Brentford score in the 1962/1963 season?

23. Who is the Bees' record League goalscorer, with 39 in the 1932/1933 season?

24. John Buttigieg is the club's most capped player, with 63 international appearances for which country?

25. Between 1949 and 1964 who made a record 514 League appearances?

26. Brentford's highest home attendance was 38,678 on 26 February 1949, but whom were they playing?

27. Jim Towers holds the record for the total number of League goals scored - how many?

28. Between September and December 2006 how many games did Brentford go without winning?

29. With how many record points did the club end the Division Two 1995 and Division Three 1999 seasons?

30. In October 1999 what was the record fee received from Wimbledon for Hermann Hreidarsson?

THE LEAGUE CUP

31. Whom did Brentford play in the 1st round in the 2008/2009 competition?

32. Which team did the Bees beat 4-2 on penalties after a 3-3 away draw in the 1st round during September 2002?

33. Following on from the previous question, which Bees defender scored two goals in the 3-3 draw in the 6th and 57th minutes?

34. With which north London team did Brentford draw 0-0 (1st leg) at home and lose 2-0 (away) during the 2nd round in September 2000?

35. During August 1991 with which team did Brentford draw 5-5 away in the 1st leg of the 1st round, and then beat them 3-1 at home in the 2nd leg?

36. Can you name the team that Brentford beat 2-0 away (1st leg) and 2-0 away (2nd leg) in the 1st round during August 1994?

37. Which team did Brentford beat 5-4 on aggregate in the 1st round (a 3-2 win at home and a 2-2 draw away) during August 1995?

38. Which team did the Bees beat 4-3 on penalties after a 2-2 draw away during August 2006 in the 1st round?

39. Which East Anglian-based team did Brentford beat 1-0 at home in the 1st round during August 2001, with Kevin O'Connor scoring in the 90th minute?

40. During August 1997 Brentford beat Shrewsbury Town 5-3 away in the 1st round, 2nd leg. Can you name the two Brentford players who scored a brace in the game?

CLUB HONOURS

Match the year to the honour

41.	*Division One finished 5th*	*2001*
42.	*League Division Four Champions*	*1942*
43.	*League Cup 4th round*	*1989*
44.	*League Division Three Champions*	*1936*
45.	*FA Cup Quarter Finalist*	*1938*
46.	*League Division Two Champions*	*1963*
47.	*Division Three South Champions*	*1999*
48.	*League Trophy Runners-up*	*1983*
49.	*London War Cup Winners*	*1935*
50.	*Empire Exhibition Trophy Quarters Finalist*	*1933*

KEN COOTE

51.   Ken holds the record for playing the most games for Brentford. How many did he play for the Bees – 459, 559 or 659?

52.   Which Bees manager handed Ken his debut?

53.   In what position did Ken play?

54.   How many League goals did Ken score for the Bees during his career?

55.   Against which London team did Ken make his Brentford debut on the opening day of the 1949/1950 season?

56.   Against which team did Ken score his first Brentford goal, in a 4-1 away defeat in 1949?

57.   During which season did Ken captain Brentford in their Fourth Division title success?

58.   Following on from the previous question, what award did Ken win personally at Griffin Park?

59.   How old was Ken when he retired from playing football?

60.   Following on from the previous question, what job did Ken take after retiring from the game?

WHERE DID THEY GO? - 1

Match the player to the club he joined from Brentford

61.	Andy Sinton	Oxford United
62.	Dean Holdsworth	Chelsea
63.	Marcus Bent	Queens Park Rangers
64.	Mark McCammon	Rochdale
65.	Tommy Lawton	Wimbledon
66.	Ron Greenwood	Coventry City
67.	Sam Sodje	Millwall
68.	Jay Tabb	Reading
69.	Rob Quinn	Arsenal
70.	Lee Thorpe	Crystal Palace

2008/2009

71. Who scored Brentford's first goal of the season?

72. Who scored the final penalty when Brentford beat Yeovil in the Johnstones Paint Trophy during August 2008?

73. Who was sent off 15 minutes after coming on as a substitute against Dagenham & Redbridge during September 2008?

74. From which club did Marcus Bean join Brentford in July 2008?

75. Which team did the Bees beat 1-0 away from home on 23 August with Glenn Poole scoring a 10th minute penalty?

76. Which player wore the number 8 shirt during this season?

77. Which Lancashire based team did the Bees lose 1-0 to on the opening day of the League season?

78. Who was Brentford manager during this season?

79. Who were the Bees scorers in the 4-0 home win against Grimsby Town at home during August 2008?

80. Which player wore the number 19 shirt during this season?

MANAGERS – 1

*Match the manager with the period he was
in charge at the club*

81.	David Webb	**1967-69**
82.	Martin Allen	**1949-52**
83.	Mike Everitt	**1976-80**
84.	Fred Halliday	**1993-97**
85.	Ron Noades	**2001-02**
86.	William Lewis	**1998-2000**
87.	Jimmy Sirrel	**1915-21**
88.	Steve Coppell	**1973-75**
89.	Jackie Gibbons	**2004-06**
90.	Bill Dodgin Jnr	**1900-03**

2007/2008

91. Which team did the Bees play on the opening day of the season, the match finishing in a 1-1 home draw?

92. Which team did Brentford beat 3-1 at home during February 2008, with Glenn Poole, Matthew Heywood and Alan Connell scoring?

93. Which former England captain started this season as manager of Brentford and then left in December 2007?

94. Following on from the previous question, who took over when this manager left?

95. Who was the club's top goalscorer, with 14 League goals?

96. Following on from the previous question, who was the only other player to score double figures in the League, with 12 goals?

97. In what position in the League did the Bees finish?

98. Which forward did Brentford sign from Brighton in January 2008 for £35,000?

99. How many of their 46 League games did the Bees win – 17, 18 or 19?

100. Who scored the winner in the 3-2 away win against Macclesfield during February 2008?

NATIONALITIES – 1

Match the player with his nationality

101.	Patrick Agyemang	Nigerian
102.	Hermann Hreidarsson	Welsh
103.	Ibrahima Sonko	Maltese
104.	Dudley Campbell	Icelandic
105.	Deon Burton	Irish
106.	Jay Tabb	Scottish
107.	John Buttigieg	Ghanaian
108.	Idris Hopkins	Jamaican
109.	Chic Brodie	English
110.	Sam Sodje	Senegalese

WHO AM I? – 2

111. I was the first Brentford manager and was in charge of the club between May 1903 and May 1906.

112. I am a goalkeeper who made 73 League appearances for the Bees, I have won full caps for my country Iceland and I made my debut for Brentford in 2000.

113. I made 149 League appearances for Brentford, scoring 28 goals, and I went on to play in midfield for Queens Park Rangers, Sheffield Wednesday, Spurs and Wolves.

114. I signed for the Bees in January 2008 from Brighton and I scored on my debut in February 2008 in the 3-2 away win against Mansfield Town.

115. I won 50 Republic of Ireland caps in my career and won 2 FA Cup and 1 UEFA Cup medals with Spurs. I signed for the Bees in 1992 and made 32 League appearances.

116. I started my career at Spurs and played for Colchester United between July 1999 and June 2004. I signed for Brentford in June 2007 from Hibernian.

117. I signed for the Bees in July 2008 from Southend United. I am a centre forward and was born in 1981.

118. My stay at Brentford was very short, I only played four League games in 2004/05 season before moving on to Wycombe Wanderers?

119. I made only 3 League appearances for Brentford whilst on loan in March 1988. I went on to play for various clubs including Newcastle United and Spurs and won 17 England caps in my career.

120. I managed Brentford between August 1952 and January 1953.

WHERE DID THEY COME FROM? – 1

Match the player with the club from which he joined Brentford

121.	Steve Perryman	Blackpool
122.	Dudley Campbell	Fulham
123.	Tommy Finney	Swindon Town
124.	Danny Cullip	Oxford United
125.	Ian Holloway	Torquay United
126.	Steve Claridge	Yeading
127.	Micky Droy	Wimbledon
128.	Fred Morley	Cambridge United
129.	Charlie Oatway	Crystal Palace
130.	Pat Terry	Brighton & Hove Albion

MANAGERS OF THE BEES

Rearrange the letters to spell out the name of a former manager of the Bees

131. DHCRRAI YXMNLEUO

132. DREF LLAGHAANC

133. DNAY TTCOS

134. ILLYB AYRG

135. KIEM VTTIREE

136. NOR NSEDOA

137. HILP DRLEHO

138. YRRHA RSTCUI

139. EAKCIJ BBNSGOI

140. VADID BBWE

POSITIONS IN LEAGUE TWO

*Match the season/points with the position in
which Brentford finished*

141.	1993-94, 58 points	4th
142.	2003-04, 53 points	1st
143.	1947-48, 40 points	21st
144.	1934-35, 61 points	16th
145.	1951-52, 42 points	2nd
146.	1994-95, 85 points	9th
147.	2001-02, 83 points	15th
148.	1949-50, 43 points	10th
149.	1933-34, 51 points	17th
150.	1997-98, 50 points	3rd

MATCH THE YEAR – 1

Match up the event with the year in which it took place

151.	Steve Coppell left as Brentford manager	1957
152.	Steve Sidwell was born	2002
153.	Steve Perryman took over as Bees manager	1982
154.	Keith Millen made his first team debut	1993
155.	Steve Hunt was signed for the Bees by Steve Coppell	2004
156.	Chris Kamara was born	1928
157.	Frank McLintock took over as Brentford manager	2001
158.	Wally Downes left Griffin Park as manager	1987
159.	Kevin Dearden signed for the Bees	1984
160.	Jimmy Hill was born	1985

POSITIONS IN LEAGUE THREE

Match the season/points with the position in
which Brentford finished

161.	1991-92, 82 points	17th
162.	1979-80, 41 points	22nd
163.	1963-64, 44 points	13th
164.	1972-73, 37 points	6th
165.	1965-66, 32 points	19th
166.	1958-59, 57 points	1st
167.	1984-85, 62 points	7th
168.	1988-89, 68 points	3rd
169.	1960-61, 43 points	23rd
170.	1990-91, 76 points	16th

2006/2007

171.   Who scored the winning goal in the 89th minute in the 4-3 home win against Port Vale during April 2007?

172.   Following on from the previous question, which Bees player scored a brace in the game?

173.   How many of their 46 League games did Brentford win?

174.   Which striker did Brentford sign from Sheffield United in January 2007?

175.   Who finished as the Bees' top League scorer, with 12 goals?

176.   True or false: Brentford were unbeaten in the League during August 2006?

177.   Can you name the three managers who were in charge during this season?

178.   Which forward scored a brace in the 3-1 away win against Blackpool during February 2007?

179.   In what position in the League did Brentford finish – 20th, 22nd or 24th?

180.   Who scored the only goal in the 1-0 home win against Brighton during February 2007?

SQUAD NUMBERS 2008/2009 - 1

Match the player with his squad number for the season

181.	Glenn Poole	10
182.	Marcus Bean	25
183.	Charlie MacDonald	1
184.	Lewis Ochoa	11
185.	Ben Hamer	9
186.	Craig Pead	12
187.	Nathan Elder	4
188.	Ryan Dickson	8
189.	Gary Smith	17
190.	Alan Connell	3

GOALKEEPERS

191. Can you name the two goalkeepers that had the sur name 'Brown' during 2008/2009?

192. Who made 44 League appearances for Brentford during 1996/1997?

193. Which goalkeeper signed from Grimsby Town in July 1998?

194. For whom did the Bees pay Sheffield United £60,000 in July 1990 (he also had a second spell at the club in 1997)?

195. Who joined the Bees from Carlisle United in a swap with David McKellar in 1983?

196. Who had three spells at the club, from 1972 to 1974, 1975 to 1977 and 1981 to 1982?

197. Who signed for Brentford in 1984 from Barnet and left in 1988 for Reading?

198. Which goalkeeper signed from Tottenham in 1988 for £60,000 and left Griffin Park in 1991?

199. Who played for the Bees between 1945 and 1954, after previously playing for both Arsenal and Oxford, and made 116 League appearances for the club?

200. Which goalkeeper was the only Brentford player to be ever present during the 1932/1933 Championship?

WHERE DID THEY GO? – 2

Match the player to the club he joined from Brentford

201.	Carl Asaba	Crystal Palace
202.	Nicky Forster	Stevenage Borough
203.	Deon Burton	Queens Park Rangers
204.	Alan Julian	Bedford Town
205.	Jimmy Hill	Birmingham City
206.	George Stobbart	Aldershot Town
207.	Ricky Newman	Arsenal
208.	Darren Powell	Rotherham United
209.	Henry White	Fulham
210.	Barry Silkman	Reading

PETER GELSON

211.   In what position did Peter play during his playing career?

212.   How many League goals did Peter score during his Bees career?

213.   In which year was Peter born in Hammersmith – 1940, 1941 or 1942?

214.   How many League appearances did Peter make for the Bees – 147, 471 or 714?

215.   True or false: Peter was awarded two testimonials whilst at Brentford?

216.   Peter first played for Brentford as a part-time player. What was his day job?

217.   During which season did Peter make his Brentford debut?

218.   Following on from the previous question, how many appearances did Peter make for the club in that season – 20, 24 or 28?

219.   True or false: Peter won promotion from Division Four twice during his career with Brentford?

220.   What did Peter do on three occasions during the 1965/1966 season whilst at Brentford?

NATIONALITIES – 2

Match the player with his nationality

221.	Stephen Hunt	Australian
222.	Marcus Gayle	Icelandic
223.	Chris Kamara	Polish
224.	Lloyd Owusu	English
225.	Paul Evans	Jamaican
226.	Ivar Ingimarsson	Irish
227.	Stewart Houston	Canadian
228.	Adam Griffiths	Ghanaian
229.	Gordon Sweetzer	Welsh
230.	Zbigniew Kruszynski	Scottish

JAMIE BATES

231.   In which year was Jamie born in Croydon – 1966, 1967 or 1968?

232.   How many League appearances did Jamie make for the Bees during his career – 319, 419 or 519?

233.   Against which team did Jamie make his Bees debut during September 1986?

234.   In what position did Jamie play during his playing career?

235.   Which manager handed Jamie his Brentford debut?

236.   In how many of the club's 46 League games during the 1991/1992 promotion season did Jamie play?

237.   To which team did Jamie transfer from Brentford in March 1999?

238.   How many League goals did Jamie score for Brentford during his career?

239.   Jamie scored two goals during the 1996/1997 for Brentford, against which two opponents?

240.   Jamie scored the first of the club's three goals in the 3-1 home win against Plymouth Argyle in the League during January 1998, but which two other players scored for the Bees?

MANAGERS – 2

Match the manager with the period he was in charge at the club

241.	Malcolm MacDonald	1926-49
242.	Fred Halliday	1984-87
243.	Bill Dodgin Snr	1957-65
244.	Wally Downes	1912-15
245.	Billy Gray	2002-04
246.	Steve Perryman	1903-06
247.	Dick Molyneux	1953-57
248.	Harry Curtis	1987-90
249.	Ephraim Rhodes	1908-12
250.	Frank McLintock	1966-67

1990s

251. Who managed the Bees between May 1993 and August 1997?

252. In what position did Brentford finish in the League during 1996/1997?

253. Eddie May managed the Bees for 16 games between August 1997 and November 1997, but how many games did the club win?

254. Which club did Brentford beat 2-1 at home on the opening day of the 1993/1994 season?

255. Who scored 22 League goals during 1998/1999 during his 42 starts and 4 substitute appearances?

256. Which club did the Bees beat 5-1 away on the opening day of the 1994/1995 season?

257. Who managed Brentford between November 1997 and May 1998?

258. In what position did Brentford finish in the League during 1993/1994?

259. Which defender did Brentford sign from Colchester United in October 1993?

260. Who finished as Brentford's top League scorer during 1997/1998, with 13 goals?

WHERE DID THEY COME FROM? – 2

*Match the player with the club from
which he joined Brentford*

261.	Andy Myers	West Ham United
262.	Tommy Baldwin	Hereford United
263.	Ron Harris	Colchester United
264.	Frank Dudley	Watford
265.	Ian Bolton	Northampton Town
266.	Roger Frude	Leyton Orient
267.	Gavin Mahon	Chelsea
268.	Stan Bowles	Cardiff City
269.	Chris Hughton	Manchester United
270.	Gordon Riddick	Mansfield Town

2005/2006

271. Who was Brentford's manager during this season?

272. In what position did Brentford finish in the League – 3rd, 5th or 7th?

273. Which two Essex-based sides finished 1st and 2nd and got automatic promotion?

274. Which team were the Bees playing when they won 2-0 at home on the opening day of the season?

275. Which Midlands team did Brentford beat 5-0 at home during February 2006?

276. Which forward did the Bees sign from Peterborough United during January 2006?

277. The club's top League goalscorer was Lloyd Owusu, but how many goals did he score?

278. Which forward scored 9 League goals in 13 starts and 10 substitute appearances?

279. True or false: Brentford were unbeaten in their six League matches during March 2006?

280. By which team was Brentford beaten 3-1 in the play-off semi-finals over the two legs?

FA CUP WINS

Match the season/round with the score

281. *1926-27, 3rd round*   **Birmingham City 1-3 Brentford**

282. *1963-64, 3rd round*   **Cardiff City 1-2 Brentford**

283. *1988-89, 4th round*   **Brentford 3-1 Fulham**

284. *2002-03, 3rd round*   **Hartlepool United 0-1 Brentford**

285. *1930-31, 3rd round replay*   **Brentford 2-1 Middlesbrough**

286. *1937-38, 3rd round*   **Brentford 1-0 Derby County**

287. *1975-76, 2nd round*   **Brentford 2-0 Barnsley**

288. *1958-59, 3rd round*   **Oldham Athletic 2-4 Brentford**

289. *1990-91, 2nd round*   **Wimbledon 0-2 Brentford**

290. *2004-05, 4th round replay*   **Brentford 3-1 Manchester City**

2004/2005

291. Who was Brentford manager during this season?

292. In what position did Brentford finish in the League – 2nd, 4th or 6th?

293. Can you name the Brentford goalscorers in the 4-3 home win during August 2004 against Doncaster Rovers?

294. True or false: Brentford won their final two matches of the League season?

295. Who scored a last-minute equaliser for Brentford in the 3-3 home draw against Sheffield Wednesday during February 2005?

296. Jay Smith left Brentford in October 2004 and joined which team?

297. Who scored Brentford's winner in the 2-1 home win against Swindon Town during January 2005?

298. Who was the club's top scorer, with 10 League goals?

299. Which well-travelled striker did Brentford sign from Brighton in December 2004, only for him to leave in February 2005?

300. Can you name the two players who scored in the 2-1 home win against Bournemouth during September 2004?

POSITIONS IN DIVISION FOUR

Match the season/points with the position in which Brentford finished

301.	1977-78, 56 points	19th
302.	1962-63, 62 points	11th
303.	1974-75, 49 points	4th
304.	1966-67, 49 points	5th
305.	1976-77, 43 points	1st
306.	1968-69, 48 points	15th
307.	1967-68, 43 points	3rd
308.	1973-74 40 points	8th
309.	1970-71, 59 points	14th
310.	1969-70, 56 points	9th

GERRY CAKEBREAD

311. In which year was Gerry born in Acton – 1935, 1936 or 1937?

312. In what position did Gerry play during his playing career?

313. How many League appearances did Gerry make for the Bees – 348, 358 or 368?

314. Which team did Gerry support as a youngster?

315. In which year did Gerry sign a semi-professional contract with Brentford – 1953, 1955 or 1957?

316. Gerry set a club record by playing how many consecutive games between 1958 and 1963 – 107, 187 or 267?

317. True or false: Gerry was twice selected as a reserve for England's Under-23's?

318. How many FA Cup games did Gerry play during his Brentford career – 20, 30 or 40?

319. What award did Gerry receive from the Queen during his career and his work on hydrographics?

320. True or false: Gerry played in the FA Youth Cup semi-finals in 1952 for Brentford?

WHEN WE WENT OUT
OF THE FA CUP

Match the fixture with the final score

321.	*1937-38, quarter-final, home,* *v. Preston North End*	*1-3*
322.	*1954-55, 4th round, away,* *v. Newcastle United*	*4-0*
323.	*2004-05, 5th round replay,* *home, v. Southampton*	*0-3*
324.	*1995-96, 4th round, away,* *v. Charlton Athletic*	*2-1*
325.	*1970-71, 5th round, away,* *v. Hull City*	*3-2*
326.	*1948-49, quarter-final, home,* *v. Leicester City*	*1-0*
327.	*1926-27, 5th round, away,* *v. Reading*	*3-2*
328.	*1958-59, 4th round, away,* *v. West Bromwich Albion*	*3-2*
329.	*1988-89, quarter-final, away,* *v. Liverpool*	*0-2*
330.	*2005-06, 3rd round, away,* *v. Stockport County*	*2-0*

MATCH THE YEAR – 2

Match up the event with the year in which it took place

331.	Adam Newton signed for Brentford from Peterborough United	1940
332.	Richard Cadette signed for the Bees	2007
333.	Mike Everitt took over as manager of Brentford	2004
334.	Ivar Ingimarsson signed for Brentford from IBV Vestmanneyjar	1953
335.	Gary Blissett left Griffin Park for Wimbledon	1973
336.	Tommy Lawton took over as manager in January until September	1988
337.	Glenn Poole signed for Brentford from Grays	1989
338.	Ronald Fenton was born	1999
339.	Martin Allen bought Sam Sodje for Brentford from Margate	1993
340.	Andy Sinton left Griffin Park for Queens Park Rangers	2008

SQUAD NUMBERS 2008/2009 - 2

Match the player with his squad number

341. Fraser Franks   16

342. Mark Phillips   14

343. Brett Johnson   7

344. Ross Montague   5

345. Moses Ademola   22

346. Alan Bennett   19

347. Sebastien Brown   23

348. Karleigh Osborne   6

349. Adam Newton   24

350. Sam Wood   31

2003/2004

351. Who started as manger of the Bees but left in March 2004?

352. Following on from the previous question, who took over as manager of Brentford in March 2004?

353. In which position did Brentford finish in the League – 15th, 17th or 19th?

354. True or false: Brentford lost their first four League games, conceding 12 goals?

355. Which Essex-based team did Brentford beat 3-2 at home during April 2004?

356. Who scored two penalties against Brighton in the 4-0 home win during October 2003?

357. Steve Hunt finished as Brentford's top League scorer, but with how many goals?

358. Who scored the goal when Brentford beat Bournemouth 1-0 on the final day of the season?

359. Who scored a brace in the 4-2 home win against Luton Town during October 2003?

360. Which team did Brentford beat 2-0 away during April 2004?

TOP LEAGUE APPEARANCES

*Match the player with the number of League
appearances he made for the club*

361.	Keith Millen	325
362.	Peter Gelson	317
363.	Tommy Higginson	374
364.	Alan Hawley	419
365.	Ken Coote	305
366.	Gerry Cakebread	316
367.	Jackie Graham	471
368.	Jamie Bates	388
369.	Danis Salman	514
370.	Alan Nelmes	348

JACKIE GRAHAM

371. In which year was Jackie born in Glasgow – 1944, 1945 or 1946?

372. How many League goals did Jackie score for Brentford in his career?

373. In what position did Jackie play during his playing days?

374. True or false: Jackie was voted the players' Player of the Year following the promotion campaigns of 1971/1972 and 1977/1978?

375. At which Scottish club did Jackie start his career?

376. For which team did Jackie play when he left Brentford?

377. How many League appearances did Jackie make for Brentford during his career – 373, 374 or 375?

378. From which team did Brentford sign Jackie?

379. Which Bees manager brought Jackie to the club and gave him his Brentford debut?

380. Against which team did Brentford play in Jackie's testimonial match during May 1982?

YEARS AT THE CLUB - 1

Match the player with the period he spent at the club

381.	Jamie Bates	1961-75
382.	Gerry Cakebread	2001-05
383.	Idris Hopkins	1986-99
384.	Stuart Nelson	1971-79
385.	Mike Allen	1949-54
386.	Ken Coote	1938-47
387.	Alf Jefferies	1954-64
388.	Peter Gelson	2003-07
389.	George Wilkins	1949-64
390.	Steve Hunt	1932-47

2002/2003

391. Who was Brentford's manager during this season?

392. In what position did Brentford finish in the League – 16th, 17th or 18th?

393. True or false: Brentford were unbeaten in the League during August 2002?

394. Which team did Brentford beat 2-0 away from home on the opening day of the season?

395. Who was the club's highest scorer, with 10 League goals?

396. In November 2002 which Lancashire team did Brentford beat 5-0 at home?

397. Following on from the previous question, which two players scored a brace in the game?

398. Which team did Brentford beat 3-0 during March 2003, with Matt Somner, Martin Rowlands and Steve Hunt scoring?

399. Can you name the two players, a midfielder and a forward, who both scored seven League goals during the season?

400. Which striker did Brentford sign in March 2003 from Sheffield Wednesday?

TOP LEAGUE GOALSCORERS

*Match the player with the number of League
goals he scored for the club*

401.	Gary Blissett	74
402.	Lloyd Owusu	119
403.	Jim Towers	63
404.	Billy Scott	77
405.	Steve Phillips	76
406.	Billy Dare	153
407.	George Francis	79
408.	John Lane	83
409.	Idris Hopkins	65
410.	Jack Holliday	124

1980s

411. Who was Frank McLintock's last signing as Bees manager (a loan signing) in 1987?

412. Which striker cost £80,000 in 1988 from Sheffield United?

413. In what year did the club play in the Freight Rover Trophy final at Wembley?

414. Following on from the previous question, by which team were the Bees beaten in the final?

415. Which utility player nicknamed 'Jimbo' played for the Bees between 1978 and 1984, then moving on to Exeter City?

416. In what year during the 1980s was Eddie Hutchinson born?

417. In what year did the club reach the FA Cup quarter-finals, only to be knocked out by Liverpool?

418. Which midfielder signed for Brentford in 1987 from Chelsea and made 169 League appearances, scoring 13 goals for the Bees during his career, and then left in 1991 for Southend United?

419. In what year during the 1980s was Ibrahima Sonko born?

420. In what year did Stan Bowles sign for the Bees from Leyton Orient?

BILL GORMAN

421. Bill was born on 13 July in which year – 1909, 1911 or 1913?

422. In what position did Bill play?

423. By the age of 19 Bill had become completely bald, a distinguishing feature that attracted what nickname?

424. Bill made his English League debut in 1936 for which club, making 52 League appearances over his two-year spell there?

425. In August 1938 Bill moved to Brentford, for what transfer fee?

426. How many League appearances did Bill make for the Bees from 1938 to 1950 – 125, 135 or 145?

427. Bill played for both of the Irish State Football Association teams, making how many appearances for them both between 1936 and 1948?

428. Bill made his Republic of Ireland debut on 17 March 1936 in a 1-0 home win against Switzerland, and his Northern Ireland debut was on 28 September 1946 in a 7-2 defeat against which team?

429. In October 1950 Bill became player/manager, and then in 1952 full-time manager, of which Kent club?

430. In 1955 Bill left football and went back to Bury to work, but he did carry out some unofficial scouting work for his friend George Poyser who was manager at which club?

ALAN HAWLEY

431. In what position did Alan play during his playing days?

432. How old was Alan when he made his first team debut for Brentford?

433. In which year was Alan born in Woking – 1946, 1947 or 1948?

434. How many League appearances did Alan make for Brentford – 317, 327 or 337?

435. True or false: Alan was ever present for Brentford during 1967/1968 and again in 1969/1970?

436. How many League goals did Alan score during his Brentford career – 4, 14 or 40?

437. True or false: When Alan made his Brentford debut he was the youngest person ever to play for Brentford?

438. Against which team did Alan make his debut whilst playing for Brentford in a 2-1 win during September 1962?

439. Which team were Brentford playing when Alan played his last game for the Bees during January 1974 at Griffin Park?

440. Against which London team did Brentford play in Alan's testimonial match in May 1974?

ROBERT TAYLOR

441. Where was Robert born – Norwich, Ipswich or King's Lynn?

442. Before his career took off in 1991 Robert played for which two other clubs but never made the first team?

443. On 24 March 1994 Robert joined Brentford for £100,000, from which club?

444. How many League appearances did Robert make for the Bees – 158, 168 or 178?

445. How many League goals did Robert score in his Brentford career?

446. On 27 February 1999 Robert scored all five goals away against Burnley, but which team was he playing for at the time?

447. Following on from the previous question, while at this club Robert scored a goal in the 1999 League Three play-off final at Wembley against Manchester City, but what was the result?

448. During his career Robert had two £1m-plus moves - on 29 November 1999 and on 15 August 2000 - to which two clubs?

449. In 2003 at which club did Robert finish his League-playing career, making only eight appearances for them?

450. On 21 April 2008 Robert was appointed manager of which Norfolk non-League club?

1970s

451. Which manager left Griffin Park in July 1973?

452. Who made his Bees debut at the age of 15 against Watford during November 1975?

453. Who captained the Bees to the 5th round of the FA Cup in 1971?

454. For which centre half did Brentford pay Torquay United £20,000 in March 1977?

455. Which manager took over in September 1976 and managed the club until April 1980?

456. In which two seasons during the 1970s did the club win promotion?

457. In what year was Nicky Forster born – 1971, 1972 or 1973?

458. Which ex-West Ham legend only played 38 minutes for the Bees in his career during 1976?

459. Which fullback signed from Fulham in 1976 and made 123 League appearances for the Bees between 1976 and 1980?

460. Which international signed for the Bees in 1976 for £3,000, making 140 League appearances in his Brentford career and scoring 7 goals?

NEIL SMILLIE

461. Neil was born on 19 July in which year – 1954, 1956 or 1958?

462. In which Yorkshire town was Neil born?

463. At which club did Neil start his professional career in 1975?

464. The high point of Neil's career came in the 1983 FA Cup final, when he played for Brighton & Hove Albion against whom?

465. In 1978-79 Neil played in the North American soccer league for which team?

466. In 1988 Neil moved to Brentford from which club?

467. Including a brief loan spell at Brentford in 1977 and his five years at the club between 1988 and 1993, how many League appearances did Neil make – 170, 175 or 180?

468. In 1993 Neil left Brentford and moved to Gillingham under Mike Flanagan, but what was his role there?

469. Which club did Neil manage between 1996 and 1999?

470. True or false: Neil is the son of former Barnsley and Lincoln City player Ron Smillie?

2001/2002

471. Who was the manager of Brentford during this season?

472. In what position did the Bees finish in the League – 2nd, 3rd or 4th?

473. How many League goals did Lloyd Owusu score during the season, finishing as top scorer at Griffin Park?

474. Following on from the previous question, who were the only other two players that scored double figures during the League season?

475. Who scored a last-minute goal in the 1-0 home win against Norwich City during August 2001?

476. Which team did Brentford beat 4-0 at home during January 2002?

477. Following on from the previous question, who scored twice in the game for the Bees?

478. Which team did the Bees beat 2-1 on aggregate in the play-off semi-finals over two legs?

479. Which two players scored a brace in the 5-1 home win against Bury during October 2001?

480. Which team beat Brentford 2-0 in the play-off final?

RON GREENWOOD

481. Ron was born on 11 November in which year – 1917, 1919 or 1921?

482. In what position did Ron play?

483. During World War II Ron was based in Northern Ireland where he served in the RAF, guesting for which team while there?

484. Ron signed for Brentford, the team he had supported as a boy, from which club?

485. Ron played for four clubs during his playing career, but made the most League appearances for the Bees. How many appearances did he make for the club – 142, 152 or 162?

486. During his playing career Ron only ever scored one League goal - for which club?

487. In May 1955 Ron won a First Division winners medal under a team managed by Ted Drake - which team?

488. Ron successfully managed which team from 1961 to 1974, winning the FA Cup in 1964 and the European Cup Winners Cup in 1965?

489. Ron was appointed England manager in 1977, but whom did he succeed?

490. Ron passed away on 9 February 2006, aged 84, but later that year he received what posthumous honour?

JIM TOWERS

491. In which year was Jim born in Shepherds Bush – 1930, 1933 or 1936?

492. How many League goals did Jim score during his Brentford career – 153, 163 or 173?

493. Jim scored four goals in a 6-0 away win against which club in March 1959?

494. Jim was known as one of the 'Terrible Twins', but who was the other?

495. How many League appearances did Jim make for the Bees during his career – 260, 262 or 264?

496. Against which team did Jim make his Bees debut in August 1954?

497. Following on from the previous question, which Brentford manager gave Jim his debut?

498. How many League goals did Jim score for Brentford during 1959/1960?

499. Which London team did Jim sign for when he left Griffin Park?

500. How many League goals did Jim score for Brentford during 1960/1961 – 21, 25 or 29?

ANDY SINTON

501. Andy was born in which county – Cumbria, Northumberland or Yorkshire?

502. Andy made his League debut at the age of 16 years 228 days in 1982, for which team?

503. Andy signed for Brentford on 13 December 1985, for what transfer fee?

504. Andy scored 28 League goals while at Brentford, but how many League appearances did he make?

505. After spending four seasons at Griffin Park Andy was transferred for £350,000 to Queens Park Rangers on 23 March 1989, but which manager signed him?

506. True or false: Andy played for Queens Park Rangers in 1992, the first year of the Premiership?

507. Andy came on as a substitute in the 89th minute of the 1999 League Cup final for Tottenham Hotspur at Wembley, resulting in a 1-0 win over which team?

508. In November 1991 Andy made his England debut away in a 1-1 draw with which team?

509. How many England international appearances did Andy make – 8, 10 or 12?

510. In 2004 which Hampshire non-League team did Andy manage?

HAT-TRICKS

*Match up the fixture with the player who scored
a hat-trick for the club*

511. *v. Rotherham (Home), League,
      January 1990, won 4-2*   Joe Allon

512. *v. Shrewsbury Town (Away), League,
      August 1996, won 3-0*   Dean
                                              Holdsworth

513. *v. Gainsborough (Home), FA Cup,
      November 2003, won 7-1*   Joe Allon

514. *v. Bristol Rovers (Home), League,
      January 1994, lost 4-3*   Lloyd Owusu

515. *v. Chester City (Away), League,
      December 1994, won 4-1*   Dean
                                              Holdsworth

516. *v. Leyton Orient (Home), League,
      August 1991, won 4-3*   Matt Harrold

517. *v. Southend United (Home), League,
      November 1998, won 4-1*   Carl Asaba

518. *v. Bristol Rovers (Away), League,
      February 1994, won 4-1*   Denny Mundee

519. *v. Rotherham United (Away), League,
      February 1999, won 4-2*   Nicky Forster

520. *v. Derby County (Home), Anglo Italian Cup,
      February 1993, lost 4-3*   Lloyd Owusu

IDRIS HOPKINS

521. Idris was born on 11 October in which year – 1908, 1910 or 1912?

522. At which club did Idris start his football career in 1927?

523. In what position did Idris play, wearing the number seven shirt?

524. Idris signed for the Bees in 1932 from which club, having made only four League appearances for them?

525. Idris spent 15 seasons at the club, making how many League appearances – 172, 272 or 372?

526. In his Brentford career Idris averaged a goal every three-and-a-half games, clocking up a total of how many League goals?

527. On 22 October 1938 at Ninian Park, Cardiff, Idris played in the 4-2 victory over England and scored a goal, but who scored the two England goals?

528. How many international appearances did Idris make, including wartime internationals?

529. Idris finished his playing career with Bristol City in 1947, retiring from football at what age?

530. In what year was Hopkins inducted into the Brentford Hall of Fame?

2000/2001

531. Who started the season as the club's manager, up until November 2000?

532. Following on from the previous question, who took over as Brentford manager?

533. In what position did Brentford finish in the League – 14th, 15th or 16th?

534. How many League goals did Andy Scott score to finish as the club's top goalscorer?

535. Which club did Andy Woodman sign for during January 2001?

536. Who scored a brace in the 3-2 home win against Bournemouth during September 2000?

537. Who scored the only goal in the 1-0 home win against Wrexham during March 2001?

538. Which team did Brentford beat 3-1 on the last day of the season?

539. Which team did Brentford beat 3-0 at home, with Andy Scott scoring two goals and Scott Partridge the other, on New Year's Day 2001?

540. Can you name the three goalscorers in the 3-1 home win against Notts County during February 2001?

TERRY HURLOCK

541. In which part of East London was Terry born?

542. Which club did Terry join as an apprentice in 1975?

543. Terry joined Brentford on 28 August 1980 from which non-League club?

544. What were Terry's two nicknames while at Brentford?

545. In his six seasons at Griffin Park Terry made 220 League appearances, scoring how many goals?

546. After Terry left Brentford he transferred to which club on 20 February 1986?

547. True or false: The Times ranked Terry in the top 50 hardest men in football?

548. In 1996 after severely breaking his right leg in two places Terry was forced to retire from football, but which club was he playing for at the time?

549. In 1989 Terry made three England B appearances against Switzerland, Iceland and which other team?

550. Between 1987 and 1990 Terry played for Millwall, but what was his nickname while at The Den?

BIG WINS – 1

Match up the fixture with Brentford's high-scoring victory

551.	v. Tranmere Rovers (Away), December 2005, League	5-0
552.	v. Camberley Town (Home), November 1998, FA Cup, 1st round	4-1
553.	v. Brighton & Hove Albion (Home), September 1991, League Cup, 2nd round, 1st leg	3-0
554.	v. Bristol Rovers (Away), December 1994, League	4-1
555.	v. Oxford United (Home), December 2000, Football League Trophy, 1st round	4-1
556.	v. Exeter City (Home), May 1999, League	4-1
557.	v. Portsmouth (Home), September 1992, League	5-1
558.	v. Walsall (Home), February 2006, League	4-1
559.	v. Bristol City (Home), October 1992, League	4-1
560.	v. Swansea City (Home), May 1999, League	5-0

DAVID McCULLOCH

561. David was born on 5 October in which year – 1911, 1913 or 1915?

562. In which Scottish town was David born?

563. At which Scottish club did David begin his senior career in 1932, playing for the next two years at Cathkin Park?

564. In 1934 David joined which club for £530, where he went on to make 57 League appearances and scored an astonishing 54 League goals?

565. In November 1935 David joined the Bees, for what transfer fee - £4,000, £6,000 or £8,000?

566. David spent three seasons at Griffin Park, where he made 117 League appearances, scoring how many League goals?

567. How many international goals did David score for Scotland?

568. During World War II David played temporary football for six different clubs. Can you name three of them?

569. At which Irish club did David finish his playing career in 1951?

570. In 1951 David went into management, but only ever managed one club until 1952 - which club was this?

1960s

571. Which inside forward signed for the Bees in 1961 from Chelsea and made 83 League appearances, scoring 36 goals?

572. Who managed the club between May 1966 and March 1967?

573. In which season did the club win promotion during the 1960s?

574. In what position did Brentford finish in the League during 1963/1964 – 14th, 16th or 18th?

575. From which club did Brentford sign Alan Mansley in 1967?

576. Who joined the Bees in July 1961, having been a former England youth international and having spent 12 years at Reading?

577. How much did Mel Scott cost Brentford when he signed from Chelsea in March 1963?

578. Which centre forward signed for the Bees in 1964 from Newport County, going on to make 35 League appearances and scoring 13 goals in his Brentford career?

579. In what position did Brentford finish in the League during 1967/1968 – 14th, 16th or 18th?

580. How many League goals did Billy McAdams score in his 75 League appearances for Brentford between 1962 and 1964?

CAPS FOR MY COUNTRY

*Match the player with the number of caps
earned while playing for his country*

581.	Idris Hopkins	17 England caps
582.	Bill Slater	2 Nigerian caps
583.	David McCulloch	53 Republic of Ireland caps
584.	Kenny Sansom	7 Scotland caps
585.	Sam Sodje	1 Scotland cap
586.	Gerry Peyton	86 England caps
587.	Alex Graham	12 Wales caps
588.	Marcus Gayle	33 Republic of Ireland caps
589.	Chris Hughton	12 England caps
590.	Graham Rix	14 Jamaican caps

POT LUCK – 1

591.   In which London borough are Brentford based?

592.   At the start of the 2008/2009 season what was the capacity at Griffin Park – 10, 763, 11,763 or 12,763?

593.   True or false: The 1930s was Brentford's most successful decade of the 21st century, with the club achieving consecutive top six finishes in the First Division?

594.   Who was appointed non-executive Chairman of Brentford on 20 January 2006?

595.   What is the club's best ever finish in top-flight football, achieved during 1935/1936 – 3rd, 4th or 5th?

596.   What is the name of the club's mascot?

597.   True or false: Brentford finished runners-up in the London War Cup during 1940/1941 and then won it a year later in 1941/1942?

598.   In 1993 which band recorded the song 'Red on White' for the team as their club song?

599.   Which London team tried to take over at the club during 1967?

600.   True or false: Rod Stewart was an apprentice at the club before he focused on his career in music?

HOW MUCH DID THEY PAY?

Match up the player with his transfer fee

601. **Bill Gorman from Bury in August 1938**   Free

602. **Gavin Mahon from Hereford United on 16 November 1998**   Free

603. **John Salako from Reading on 20 July 2004**   £75,000

604. **Leo Fortune-West from Lincoln City on 16 November 1998**   £25,000

605. **Sam Sodje from Margate on 27 May 2004**   £60,000

606. **Andy Sinton from Cambridge United on 13 December 1985**   £7,000

607. **Dudley Campbell from Yeading on 7 June 2005**   £25,000

608. **Gary Blissett from Crewe Alexandra on 26 March 1987**   Free

609. **Ian Holloway from MK Dons on 12 March 1986**   £50,000

610. **Danny Cullip from Fulham on 18 February 1998**   £60,000

GOALSCORERS – 1

Match up the player with the number of goals scored for the club

611.	Michael Allen	24
612.	Dean Holdsworth	11
613.	Mark Lazarus	25
614.	Paul Abrahams	15
615.	Nigel Gleghorn	2
616.	Marcus Gayle (both spells)	54
617.	Frank Morrad	18
618.	Patsy Hendren	8
619.	Terry Hurlock	1
620.	Earnest Muttitt	20

LLOYD OWUSU

621. Lloyd was born on 12 December in which year – 1974,
1976 or 1978?

622. Lloyd was born in a town in Berkshire where they
filmed Carry On Loving and Carry On Abroad in the
early 1970s. Can you name the town?

623. At which non-League club did Lloyd start his career?

624. Which manager signed Lloyd to play for the Bees in
1998?

625. Lloyd had two spells at Griffin Park (1998-2002) and
(2005-07), making 213 League appearances for
Brentford, but how many League goals did he score?

626. In the 2001-02 season Lloyd helped the Bees to the
League Two play-off final, where they lost 2-0 to Stoke
City. How many League goals did he score in this
season?

627. In 2005 Lloyd made two international appearances,
but for which country?

628. When Lloyd finished his second spell at Brentford in
2007, for which club did he sign on 6 July 2007?

629. After suffering a groin injury on 26 April 2006 Lloyd
did not play first team football for 11 months. He
made his comeback on 17 March 2007 in a 1-0 home
defeat against which team?

630. True or false: Lloyd is a part-time disc jockey?

1950s

631. In which year did Ian Dargie sign for Brentford – 1952, 1953 or 1954?

632. Which defender did the Bees sign in 1956 from Sunday League park team Jolly X?

633. Which team did John Paton sign for when he left Griffin Park in 1952?

634. Who managed the club between January and September 1953?

635. Which English schoolboy signed for Brentford after he was released from National Service in 1950, going on to make 40 League appearances and scoring 8 goals?

636. Which three letters does Verdi Godwin, who played for Brentford between 1952 and 1954, have after his name?

637. Which centre half was born in 1931, his Brentford career saw him make 263 League appearances, scoring 23 goals?

638. Which manager won 60 games out of his 169 in charge during the 1950s?

639. Which right back was born in 1956 and was Frank McLintock's second signing for Brentford in 1984?

640. Which Scottish winger signed from St Rochs in September 1958 and made his Bees debut at the age of 18?

PAUL EVANS

641. Paul was born on 1 September in which year – 1970, 1972 or 1974?

642. At which club did Paul start his professional career on 2 July 1993?

643. Paul signed for the Bees on 3 March 1999, for what transfer fee?

644. In the 1999-2000 season Paul scored two memorable goals, the first from 60 yards and the second from 45 yards, in consecutive games against which two opponents?

645. In his three years at Griffin Park Paul made 130 League appearances for the Bees, scoring how many League goals?

646. In what position did Paul play?

647. After leaving Brentford on 9 August 2002 which club did Paul join on a free transfer?

648. How many international appearances for Wales has Paul made?

649. In July 2006 Paul was given a trial at Swindon Town, which was under whose management at the time?

650. True or false: Paul was named in the Professional Football Association League Two team in 2002?

ALAN NELMES

651. At which London club did Alan start his professional football career?

652. In what year was Alan signed for Brentford?

653. Which Bees manager signed Alan?

654. Which award did Alan win at the club during 1970/1971?

655. In which year was Alan born – 1948, 1949 or 1950?

656. How many League appearances did Alan make for Brentford – 216, 316 or 416?

657. How many seasons did Alan spend at Griffin Park?

658. How many League goals did Alan score for Brentford during his career – 1, 2 or 3?

659. How many matches did Alan miss between 1968 and 1972 – 3, 30 or 60?

660. In what year did Alan leave the club and join Hillingdon Borough?

CHRIS KAMARA

661. Chris was born on Christmas Day in which year – 1955, 1957 or 1959?

662. In which north-east town was Chris born?

663. At which club did Chris start his professional career in 1976?

664. Chris signed for the Bees on 28 October 1981 in a straight swap with David Crown that was said to be valued at how much?

665. Chris made his Bees debut against Burnley alongside which other debutant?

666. In his four seasons at Brentford Chris made 152 League appearances, the most he made for any club, but how many League goals did he score?

667. True or false: Chris won the Player of the Year award in the 1982/1983 season?

668. At which club, whom he went on to manage, did Chris finish his playing career?

669. Chris held the post of manager at which club before becoming a football analyst on Sky Sports?

670. Which former Brentford manager does Chris work alongside on Sky Sports?

ATTENDANCES

Match up the fixture with the attendance figure

671. *v. Swansea City (Home),*
     May 2006, play-off semi-final, 2nd leg   4,596

672. *v. Crewe Alexandra (Wembley),*
     May 1997, play-off final   4,846

673. *v. Rotherham United (Home),*
     February 1996, League   6,048

674. *v. Sheffield Wednesday (Home),*
     May 2005, play-off semi-final, 2nd leg   6,246

675. *v. Huddersfield (Home),*
     May 1995, play-off semi-final, 2nd leg   10,823

676. *v. Mansfield Town (Home),*
     August 1998, League   9,485

677. *v. Bury (Home),*
     May 2001, League   34,149

678. *v. Blackpool (Home),*
     August 2006, League   3,446

679. *v. Hereford United (Home),*
     April 2008, League   10,652

680. *v. Bournemouth (Home),*
     May 2004, League   11,161

DEAN HOLDSWORTH

681. Dean was born on 8 November in which year – 1964, 1966 or 1968?

682. Where in East London was Dean born?

683. At which club did Dean start his professional career, scoring 3 League goals in 16 League appearances?

684. Which manager brought Dean to Brentford in September 1989 for £125,000?

685. Dean made 117 League appearances for the Bees, with a scoring ratio of almost a goal every two games, but how many League goals did he score?

686. In 1992 Dean moved to which Premier League club for £720,000, a transfer that included Micky Bennett and Detsi Kruszynsk going to Griffin Park?

687. Dean never made the England first team but he did make an England B appearance, scoring a goal in a 4-2 win at Hillsborough Stadium against which opponents?

688. In July 2007 Dean was appointed player/manager at which Isthmian League club?

689. In May 2008 whom did Dean succeed as manager at Newport County?

690. True or false: Dean's twin brother Donald had a successful football career, playing primarily for Watford, Sheffield United and Birmingham?

BIG WINS – 2

Match up the fixture with Brentford's high-scoring victory

691. *v. Blackpool (Home),*
      November 2002, League   **3-0**

692. *v. Bury (Home),*
      October 2001, League   **7-1**

693. *v. Shrewsbury Town (Away),*
      August 1997, League Cup, 1st round, 2nd leg   **6-0**

694. *v. Gainsborough Trinity (Home),*
      November 2003, FA Cup, 1st round   **5-1**

695. *v. Plymouth Argyle (Away),*
      August 1994, League   **7-0**

696. *v. Northampton (Home),*
      March 2003, League   **5-3**

697. *v. Plymouth Argyle (Home),*
      December 1994, League   **4-0**

698. *v. Tranmere Rovers (Home),*
      September 2001, League   **3-0**

699. *v. York City (Home),*
      April 1995, League   **5-0**

700. *v. Cambridge United (Home),*
      January 1995, League   **5-1**

MARCUS GAYLE

701.   Marcus was born on 27 September in which year –
       1970, 1972 or 1974?

702.   Marcus was born where in West London?

703.   At which club in the close season of 1989 did Marcus
       start his professional career?

704.   Marcus had two spells at Brentford, making 186
       League appearances, but how many League goals did
       he score – 20, 24 or 28?

705.   When he left the Bees after his second spell ended on
       17 May 2006 which club did Marcus join on 2 July
       2006, where he went on to make 24 League
       appearances and scored 7 League goals?

706.   What did Marcus achieve on 14 October 2006 after
       coming on as a second-half substitute against
       Kidderminster Harriers?

707.   Marcus is one of only two players to have played for
       both AFC Wimbledon and Wimbledon FC. Who is the
       other?

708.   Marcus was capped 14 times at international level and
       played in the 1998 FIFA World Cup, for which country?

709.   At which club did Marcus finish his playing career in
       May 2008 after securing promotion to the Blue Square
       Conference South by beating Staines Town 2-1 in the
       play-off final?

710.   True or false: Marcus owns a designer clothes shop
       called '3 Tribes' in Fulham Road, London?

TOMMY HIGGINSON

711. In which year was Tommy born in Newtongrange –
     1935, 1937 or 1939?

712. How many League goals did Tommy score for
     Brentford during his career?

713. Tommy joined the Bees from which Scottish team in
     1959?

714. Which Brentford manager signed Tommy and handed
     him his debut?

715. True or false: Tommy became the first post-war
     Brentford player to be sent off, whilst playing against
     Shrewsbury?

716. Which team did Brentford play in Tommy's
     testimonial in April 1969?

717. Which team did Tommy join when he left Griffin Park?

718. How many League appearances did Tommy make for
     Brentford – 368, 388 or 408?

719. In what position did Tommy play whilst at Brentford?

720. Can you name three of the five managers that Tommy
     played under whilst at Griffin Park?

GARY BLISSETT

721. Gary was born on 29 June in which year – 1962, 1964 or 1966?

722. In which north-west city was Gary born?

723. At which club did Gary start his professional career in August 1983 before moving to Brentford on 26 March 1987?

724. When Gary signed for the Bees what was his transfer fee?

725. During his six years at Griffin Park Gary made 233 League appearances, 13 of them as a substitute, but how many League goals did he score?

726. In 1992 the Bees were crowned League champions of Division Three, with Gary scoring the winning goal that clinched promotion. Against which team, who went on to win the play-offs to also gain promotion, were Brentford playing?

727. Gary once played 45 minutes as goalkeeper in the 1992/1993 season when Graham Benstead went off injured, and he managed not to concede a goal, but who were the opponents?

728. Gary joined Wimbledon on 23 July 1993, for what transfer fee?

729. In which other two countries did Gary also play League football?

730. In what position did Gary play?

POT LUCK – 2

731. True or false: Comedian Bradley Walsh was a professional player at the club in the late 1970s but didn't manage to play a first team game?

732. Who is the club's most capped player with 63 caps for Malta?

733. Can you name the player that won four Barbados caps whilst at Brentford during 1996/1997?

734. Which striker made his debut in October 1995 against Shrewsbury and went on to make a total of 70 League appearances, scoring 8 goals for the club?

735. Which defender did Brentford sign on a free transfer from Northampton Town during August 2008?

736. Which goalkeeper played for Brentford between 1963 and 1971, making 199 League appearances?

737. Following on from the previous question, which club did he sign from to join the Bees in 1963?

738. In what position did Gordon Phillips play for Brentford – goalkeeper, defender or striker?

739. How much did Dave Simmons cost Brentford in March 1974?

740. Which Senegal Under-21 international centre back did Brentford sign in 2002?

POSITIONS IN THE TEAM

Match the player with the position in which he played

741. John Burns

742. John Steel

743. Pat Kruse

744. Anthony Harper

745. Richard Parker

746. James Elliott

747. Jack Astley

748. William Relph

749. Gary Phillips

750. James Lawrence

Winger

Centre half

Midfield

Defender

Goalkeeper

Inside forward

Wing half

Centre forward

Fullback

Right back

GOALSCORERS – 2

Match up the player with the number of goals scored for the club

751.	Johnny Brooks	4
752.	John Fielding	4
753.	David Nelson	28
754.	Darren Powell	54
755.	Steve Sidwell	18
756.	Roger Cross (both spells)	15
757.	John Salako	36
758.	Gordon Neilson	18
759.	Neil Smillie (both spells)	6
760.	John O'Mara	5

YEARS AT THE CLUB – 2

Match the player with the period he spent at the club

761.	William Dobson	*1932-44*
762.	Kenneth Horne	*1977-80*
763.	Thomas Sperrin	*1983-86*
764.	Edward Ware	*1993-95*
765.	John Fielding	*1949-56*
766.	Terry Bullivant	*1928-33*
767.	Joseph Grozier	*1950-61*
768.	Jack Holliday	*1963-65*
769.	Denny Mundee	*1999-2006*
770.	Douglas Allder	*1937-49*

POT LUCK – 3

771. For which country did Niall Thompson win a full international cap whilst at Brentford during 1998?

772. How many spells at the club did Paul Priddy have – 1, 2 or 3?

773. Which London team did Robbie Cooke sign for when he left Griffin Park in 1987?

774. How much did Steve Wignall cost the Bees in 1984 - £8,000, £18,000 or £180,000?

775. Which forward did the Bees sign in July 2008 from Southend United?

776. In what position did Paul Smith play during his time at Griffin Park?

777. In which year did Bill Hodge sign for Brentford from Glasgow Rangers – 1925, 1927 or 1929?

778. How many League appearances did Stewart Houston make for the Bees during his career, scoring nine goals – 57, 67 or 77?

779. Which forward left Brentford and joined Ebbsfleet in July 2008?

780. True or false: Kevin Dearden won the players' Player of the Year award during his first season at Griffin Park, 1993/1994?

HARRY CURTIS

781. By what nickname was Harry known while at Brentford?

782. At which club did Harry start his managerial career in 1923?

783. Harry joined the Bees in May 1926 and led them to two titles - the Division Three South in 1932/1933 and the Second Division in 1934/1935. In their debut season in the First Division they finished in what position?

784. Under Harry in the 1929/1930 season the Bees recorded how many consecutive home wins?

785. Following on from the previous question, behind whom did they finish runners-up in the Third Division South?

786. Where in North London was Harry born?

787. For which two non-League clubs did he play before becoming a referee?

788. From 1918 to 1923 Harry refereed a number of League games including Brentford matches, but only ever sent off three players. One of these was the Bees' inside forward, who was the first Brentford player ever to be sent off, in February 1922, but who was he?

789. During his Brentford managerial career, where his statistics were P-660, W-284, D-150, L-226, F-1123, A-965, how many points did he accumulate – 618, 718 or 818?

790. True or false: Harry remains the Bees' most successful and longest serving manager?

GOALSCORERS – 3

Match up the player with the number of goals scored for the club

791.	James Bain	124
792.	Vivian Woodward	16
793.	Mick Block	20
794.	Brian Statham	16
795.	Paul Walker	2
796.	Stan Bowles	1
797.	Jay Tabb	4
798.	Dean Smith	5
799.	Kevin Rapley	30
800.	George Francis (both spells)	12

ANSWERS

CLUB HISTORY

1.   1889
2.   Griffin Park
3.   The Bees
4.   Brentford Rowing Club
5.   1904
6.   Third Division South
7.   Portsmouth
8.   Queens Park Rangers
9.   William Lewis
10. 20,000

WHO AM I? - 1

11. Phil Holder
12. Andrew Ansah
13. Michael Dobson
14. Roger Cross
15. Frank Dudley
16. Steve Perryman
17. Steve Wignall
18. Paul Walker
19. Hermann Hreidarsson
20. John Docherty

CLUB RECORDS

21. Wrexham
22. 98
23. Jack Holliday
24. Malta
25. Ken Coote
26. Leicester City
27. 153 (1954-61)
28. 18
29. 85
30. £2.5 million

THE LEAGUE CUP

31. Swansea City

32.	Bournemouth
33.	Kevin O'Connor
34.	Tottenham Hotspur
35.	Barnet
36.	Colchester United
37.	Walsall
38.	Swindon Town
39.	Norwich City
40.	Kevin Rapley and Robert Taylor

CLUB HONOURS

41.	Division One finished 5th	1936
42.	League Division Four Champions	1963
43.	League Cup 4th round	1983
44.	League Division Three Champions	1999
45.	FA Cup Quarter Finalist	1989
46.	League Division Two Champions	1935
47.	Division Three South Champions	1933
48.	League Trophy Runners-up	2001
49.	London War Cup Winners	1942
50.	Empire Exhibition Trophy Quarters Finalist	1938

KEN COOTE

51.	559: 514 League, 35 FA Cup and 10 League Cup
52.	Jackie Gibbons
53.	Fullback
54.	14
55.	Tottenham Hotspur
56.	Blackburn Rovers
57.	1962/1963
58.	Player of the Year
59.	37
60.	Betting shop manager

WHERE DID THEY GO? – 1

61.	Andy Sinton	Queens Park Rangers
62.	Dean Holdsworth	Wimbledon
63.	Marcus Bent	Crystal Palace

64.	Mark McCammon	Millwall
65.	Tommy Lawton	Arsenal
66.	Ron Greenwood	Chelsea
67.	Sam Sodje	Reading
68.	Jay Tabb	Coventry City
69.	Rob Quinn	Oxford United
70.	Lee Thorpe	Rochdale

2008/2009

71. Charlie MacDonald (against Grimsby Town, August 2008)
72. Ryan Dickson
73. Kevin O'Connor
74. Blackpool
75. Barnet
76. Gary Smith
77. Bury
78. Andy Scott
79. Charlie MacDonald (2), Nathan Elder and Glenn Poole
80. Moses Ademola

MANAGERS – 1

81.	David Webb	1993-97
82.	Martin Allen	2004-06
83.	Mike Everitt	1973-75
84.	Fred Halliday	1915-21
85.	Ron Noades	1998-2000
86.	William Lewis	1900-03
87.	Jimmy Sirrel	1967-69
88.	Steve Coppell	2001-02
89.	Jackie Gibbons	1949-52
90.	Bill Dodgin Jnr	1976-80

2007/2008

91. Mansfield
92. Accrington Stanley
93. Terry Butcher
94. Andy Scott
95. Glenn Poole

96.   *Alan Connell*
97.   *4th*
98.   *Nathan Elder*
99.   *17*
100.   *Nathan Elder*

NATIONALITIES – 1

101.	*Patrick Agyemang*	*Ghanaian*
102.	*Herman Hreidarsson*	*Icelandic*
103.	*Ibrahima Sonko*	*Senegalese*
104.	*Dudley Campbell*	*English*
105.	*Deon Burton*	*Jamaican*
106.	*Jay Tabb*	*Irish*
107.	*John Buttigieg*	*Maltese*
108.	*Idris Hopkins*	*Welsh*
109.	*Chic Brodie*	*Scottish*
110.	*Sam Sodje*	*Nigerian*

WHO AM I? – 2

111.   *Richard Molyneux*
112.   *Olafur Gottskalksson*
113.   *Andy Sinton*
114.   *Nathan Elder*
115.   *Chris Hughton*
116.   *Simon Brown*
117.   *Charlie MacDonald*
118.   *Steve Claridge*
119.   *Les Ferdinand*
120.   *Jimmy Bain*

WHERE DID THEY COME FROM? – 1

121.	*Steve Perryman*	*Oxford United*
122.	*Dudley Campbell*	*Yeading*
123.	*Tommy Finney*	*Cambridge United*
124.	*Danny Cullip*	*Fulham*
125.	*Ian Holloway*	*Wimbledon*
126.	*Steve Claridge*	*Brighton & Hove Albion*
127.	*Micky Droy*	*Crystal Palace*

128.	Fred Morley	Blackpool
129.	Charlie Oatway	Torquay United
130.	Pat Terry	Swindon Town

MANAGERS OF THE BEES

131.	Richard Molyneux
132.	Fred Callaghan
133.	Andy Scott
134.	Billy Gray
135.	Mike Everitt
136.	Ron Noades
137.	Phil Holder
138.	Harry Curtis
139.	Jackie Gibbons
140.	David Webb

POSITIONS IN LEAGUE TWO

141.	1993-94, 58 points	16th
142.	2003-04, 53 points	17th
143.	1947-48, 40 points	15th
144.	1934-35, 61 points	1st
145.	1951-52, 42 points	10th
146.	1994-95, 85 points	2nd
147.	2001-02, 83 points	3rd
148.	1949-50, 43 points	9th
149.	1933-34, 51 points	4th
150.	1997-98, 50 points	21st

MATCH THE YEAR – 1

151.	Steve Coppell left as Brentford manager	2002
152.	Steve Sidwell was born	1982
153.	Steve Perryman took over as Bees manager	1987
154.	Keith Millen made his first team debut	1985
155.	Steve Hunt was signed for the Bees by Steve Coppell	2001
156.	Chris Kamara was born	1957
157.	Frank McLintock took over as Brentford manager	1984
158.	Wally Downes left Griffin Park as manager	2004
159.	Kevin Dearden signed for the Bees	1993

POSITIONS IN LEAGUE THREE

161.	1991-92, 82 points	1st
162.	1979-80, 41 points	19th
163.	1963-64, 44 points	16th
164.	1972-73, 37 points	22nd
165.	1965-66, 32 points	23rd
166.	1958-59, 57 points	3rd
167.	1984-85, 62 points	13th
168.	1988-89, 68 points	7th
169.	1960-61, 43 points	17th
170.	1990-91, 76 points	6th

2006/2007

171.   Darius Charles

172.   Charlie Ide

173.   8

174.   Neil Shipperley

175.   Jo Kuffour

176.   True: 2 wins and 3 draws

177.   Leroy Resenior, Scott Fitzgerald and Barry Quinn

178.   Jo Kuffour

179.   24th

180.   Jo Kuffour

SQUAD NUMBERS 2008/2009 - 1

181.	Glenn Poole	11
182.	Marcus Bean	4
183.	Charlie MacDonald	10
184.	Lewis Ochoa	25
185.	Ben Hamer	1
186.	Craig Pead	17
187.	Nathan Elder	9
188.	Ryan Dickson	3
189.	Gary Smith	8
190.	Alan Connell	12

GOALKEEPERS

191.   Sebastien Brown and Simon Brown
192.   Kevin Dearden
193.   Jason Pearcey
194.   Graham Benstead
195.   Trevor Swinburne
196.   Paul Priddy
197.   Gary Phillips
198.   Tony Parks
199.   Alf Jefferies
200.   Tommy Baker

WHERE DID THEY GO? – 2

201.   Carl Asaba   Reading
202.   Nicky Forster   Birmingham City
203.   Deon Burton   Rotherham United
204.   Alan Julian   Stevenage Borough
205.   Jimmy Hill   Fulham
206.   George Stobbart   Bedford Town
207.   Ricky Newman   Aldershot Town
208.   Darren Powell   Crystal Palace
209.   Henry White   Arsenal
210.   Barry Silkman   Queens Park Rangers

PETER GELSON

211.   Centre half
212.   17
213.   1941
214.   471
215.   True
216.   Post office engineer
217.   1961/1962
218.   28
219.   True
220.   Scored from his own half of the pitch

NATIONALITIES – 2

221.   Stephen Hunt   Irish

222.	Marcus Gayle	Jamaican
223.	Chris Kamara	English
224.	Lloyd Owusu	Ghanaian
225.	Paul Evans	Welsh
226.	Ivar Ingimarsson	Icelandic
227.	Stewart Houston	Scottish
228.	Adam Griffiths	Australian
229.	Gordon Sweetzer	Canadian
230.	Zbigniew Kruszynski	Polish

JAMIE BATES

231.	1968
232.	419
233.	Carlisle United
234.	Centre half
235.	Frank McLintock
236.	42
237.	Wycombe Wanderers
238.	18
239.	Luton Town and Chesterfield
240.	Andy Scott and Graeme Hogg

MANAGERS – 2

241.	Malcolm MacDonald	1957-65
242.	Fred Halliday	1908-12
243.	Bill Dodgin Snr	1953-57
244.	Wally Downes	2002-04
245.	Billy Gray	1966-67
246.	Steve Perryman	1987-90
247.	Dick Molyneux	1903-06
248.	Harry Curtis	1926-49
249.	Ephraim Rhodes	1912-15
250.	Frank McLintock	1984-87

1990s

251.	David Webb
252.	4th
253.	4

254. Exeter City
255. Lloyd Owusu
256. Plymouth Argyle
257. Micky Adams
258. 16th
259. Martin Grainger
260. Rob Taylor

WHERE DID THEY COME FROM? – 2

261. Andy Myers   Colchester United
262. Tommy Baldwin   Manchester United
263. Ron Harris   Chelsea
264. Frank Dudley   Cardiff City
265. Ian Bolton   Watford
266. Roger Frude   Mansfield Town
267. Gavin Mahon   Hereford United
268. Stan Bowles   Leyton Orient
269. Chris Hughton   West Ham United
270. Gordon Riddick   Northampton Town

2005/2006

271. Martin Allen
272. 3rd
273. Southend United (1st) and Colchester United (2nd)
274. Scunthorpe United
275. Walsall
276. Callum Willock
277. 12
278. D.J. Campbell
279. False: won 3, lost 3
280. Swansea

FA CUP WINS

281. 1926-27, 3rd round   Oldham Athletic 2-4 Brentford
282. 1963-64, 3rd round   Brentford 2-1 Middlesbrough
283. 1988-89, 4th round   Brentford 3-1 Manchester City
284. 2002-03, 3rd round   Brentford 1-0 Derby County
285. 1930-31, 3rd round replay Cardiff City 1-2 Brentford

286.	1937-38, 3rd round	Brentford 3-1 Fulham
287.	1975-76, 2nd round	Wimbledon 0-2 Brentford
288.	1958-59, 3rd round	Brentford 2-0 Barnsley
289.	1990-91, 2nd round	Birmingham City 1-3 Brentford
290.	2004-05, 4th round replay	Hartlepool United 0-1 Brentford

2004/2005

291. Martin Allen

292. 4th

293. Isaiah Rankin, Chris Hargreaves, Deon Burton and Jay Tabb

294. True: against Wrexham and Hull City

295. Steve Hunt

296. Farnborough

297. Steve Hunt

298. Deon Burton

299. Steve Claridge

300. Stewart Talbot and Isaiah Rankin

POSITIONS IN DIVISION FOUR

301.	1977-78, 56 points	4th
302.	1962-63, 62 points	1st
303.	1974-75, 49 points	8th
304.	1966-67, 49 points	9th
305.	1976-77, 43 points	15th
306.	1968-69, 48 points	11th
307.	1967-68, 43 points	14th
308.	1973-74, 40 points	19th
309.	1970-71, 59 points	3rd
310.	1969-70, 56 points	5th

GERRY CAKEBREAD

311. 1936

312. Goalkeeper

313. 348

314. Brentford

315. 1955

316. 187: 168 League, 15 FA Cup and 4 League Cup

317. True

318. 20
319. OBE
320. True

WHEN WE WENT OUT OF THE FA CUP

321. 1937-38, quarter-final, home,
     v. Preston North End   0-3
322. 1954-55, 4th round, away,
     v. Newcastle United   3-2
323. 2004-05, 5th round replay, home,
     v. Southampton   1-3
324. 1995-96, 4th round, away,
     v. Charlton Athletic   3-2
325. 1970-71, 5th round, away,
     v. Hull City   2-1
326. 1948-49, quarter-final, home,
     v. Leicester City   0-2
327. 1926-27, 5th round, away,
     v. Reading   1-0
328. 1958-59, 4th round, away,
     v. West Bromwich Albion   2-0
329. 1988-89, quarter-final, away,
     v. Liverpool   4-0
330. 2005-06, 3rd round, away,
     v. Stockport County   3-2

MATCH THE YEAR – 2

331. Adam Newton signed for Brentford
     from Peterborough United   2008
332. Richard Cadette signed for the Bees   1988
333. Mike Everitt took over as manager of Brentford   1973
334. Ivar Ingimarsson signed for Brentford
     from IBV Vestmanneyjar   1999
335. Gary Blissett left Griffin Park for Wimbledon   1993
336. Tommy Lawton took over as manager
     in January until September   1953
337. Glenn Poole signed for Brentford from Grays   2007
338. Ronald Fenton was born   1940

93

339.	Martin Allen bought Sam Sodje for Brentford from Margate	2004
340.	Andy Sinton left Griffin Park for Queens Park Rangers	1989

SQUAD NUMBERS 2008/2009 - 2

341.	Fraser Franks	24
342.	Mark Phillips	5
343.	Brett Johnston	14
344.	Ross Montague	23
345.	Moses Ademola	19
346.	Alan Bennett	6
347.	Sebastien Brown	31
348.	Karleigh Osborne	22
349.	Adam Newton	7
350.	Sam Wood	16

2003/2004

351.	Wally Downes
352.	Martin Allen
353.	17th
354.	True
355.	Colchester United
356.	Steve Hunt
357.	11
358.	Alex Rhodes
359.	Jay Tabb
360.	Barnsley

TOP LEAGUE APPEARANCES

361.	Keith Millen	305
362.	Peter Gelson	471
363.	Tommy Higginson	388
364.	Alan Hawley	317
365.	Ken Coote	514
366.	Gerry Cakebread	348
367.	Jackie Graham	374
368.	Jamie Bates	419

| 369. | Danis Salman | 325 |
| 370. | Alan Nelmes | 316 |

JACKIE GRAHAM

371.	1946
372.	38
373.	Midfield
374.	True
375.	Greenock Morton
376.	Addlestone and Weybridge
377.	374
378.	Guildford City
379.	Frank Blunstone
380.	Watford

YEARS AT THE CLUB - 1

381.	Jamie Bates	1986-99
382.	Gerry Cakebread	1954-64
383.	Idris Hopkins	1932-47
384.	Stuart Nelson	2003-07
385.	Mike Allen	1971-79
386.	Ken Coote	1949-64
387.	Alf Jefferies	1949-54
388.	Peter Gelson	1961-75
389.	George Wilkins	1938-47
390.	Steve Hunt	2001-05

2002/2003

391.	Wally Downes
392.	16th
393.	True: 4 wins and 2 draws
394.	Huddersfield Town
395.	Rowan Vine
396.	Blackpool
397.	Steve Evans and Ibrahima Sonko
398.	Northampton Town
399.	Mark McCammon and Steve Hunt
400.	Efan Ekoku

TOP LEAGUE GOALSCORERS

401.	Gary Blissett	79
402.	Lloyd Owusu	76
403.	Jim Towers	153
404.	Billy Scott	83
405.	Steve Phillips	65
406.	Billy Dare	63
407.	George Francis	124
408.	John Lane	74
409.	Idris Hopkins	77
410.	Jack Holliday	119

1980s

411.	Paul Merson
412.	Richard Cadette
413.	1985
414.	Wigan Athletic
415.	Jim McNichol
416.	1982
417.	1989
418.	Keith Jones
419.	1981
420.	1981

BILL GORMAN

421.	1911
422.	Fullback
423.	Old Naked Brains
424.	Bury
425.	£7,000
426.	125
427.	17
428.	England
429.	Deal Town
430.	Manchester City

ALAN HAWLEY

431.	Fullback

432. 16
433. 1946
434. 317
435. True
436. 4
437. True: 16 years, 3 months, 22 days
438. Barrow
439. Hartlepool
440. Leyton Orient

ROBERT TAYLOR

441. Norwich
442. Norwich City and Birmingham City
443. Leyton Orient
444. 178
445. 56
446. Gillingham
447. 2-2, but Manchester City won 3-1 on penalties, 30 May 1999
448. Manchester City on 29 November 1999 and Wolverhampton Wanderers on 15 August 2000
449. Scunthorpe United
450. Diss Town

1970s

451. Frank Blunstone
452. Danis Salman
453. Bobby Ross
454. Pat Kruse
455. Bill Dodgin Jnr
456. 1971/1972 and 1977/1978
457. 1973
458. Harry Redknapp
459. John Fraser
460. Dave Carlton

NEIL SMILLIE

461. 1958
462. Barnsley

463. Crystal Palace
464. Manchester United (After a 2-2 draw Manchester won the replay 4-0)
465. Memphis Rogues
466. Reading
467. 175
468. Player/coach
469. Wycombe Wanderers
470. True

2001/2002

471. Steve Coppell
472. 3rd
473. 20
474. Ben Burgess (17) and Paul Evans (14)
475. Kevin O'Connor
476. Brighton & Hove Albion
477. Ben Burgess
478. Huddersfield
479. Lloyd Owusu and Paul Gibbs
480. Stoke City

RON GREENWOOD

481. 1921
482. Defender
483. Belfast Celtic
484. Bradford Park Avenue
485. 142
486. Brentford
487. Chelsea
488. West Ham United
489. Don Revie
490. He was inducted into the English Football Hall of Fame

JIM TOWERS

491. 1933
492. 153
493. Southampton

494. George Francis
495. 262
496. Shrewsbury Town
497. Bill Dodgin Snr
498. 23
499. Queens Park Rangers
500. 21

ANDY SINTON
501. Northumberland
502. Cambridge United
503. £25,000
504. 149
505. Trevor Francis
506. True
507. Leicester City
508. Poland
509. 12
510. Fleet Town

HAT-TRICKS
511. v. Rotherham (Home), League,
    January 1990, won 4-2   Dean Holdsworth
512. v. Shrewsbury Town (Away), League,
    August 1996, won 3-0   Carl Asaba
513. v. Gainsborough (Home), FA Cup,
    November 2003, won 7-1   Matt Harrold
514. v. Bristol Rovers (Home), League,
    January 1994, lost 4-3   Denny Mundee
515. v. Chester City (Away), League,
    December 1994, won 4-1   Nicky Forster
516. v. Leyton Orient (Home), League,
    August 1991, won 4-3   Dean Holdsworth
517. v. Southend United (Home), League,
    November 1998, won 4-1   Lloyd Owusu
518. v. Bristol Rovers (Away), League,
    February 1994, won 4-1   Joe Allon

519.	v. Rotherham United (away), League	
	February 1999, won 4-2	Lloyd Owusu
520.	v. Derby County (Home), Anglo Italian Cup,	
	February 1993, lost 4-3	Joe Allon

IDRIS HOPKINS

521.	1910
522.	Merthyr Tydfil
523.	Right wing
524.	Crystal Palace
525.	272
526.	77
527.	Stanley Matthews and Tommy Lawton
528.	21
529.	40
530.	1989

2000/2001

531.	Ron Noades
532.	Ray Lewington
533.	14th
534.	13
535.	Colchester United
536.	Andy Scott
537.	Darren Powell
538.	Bury
539.	Oxford United
540.	Paul Evans, Lloyd Owusu and Scott Partridge

TERRY HURLOCK

541.	Hackney
542.	West Ham United
543.	Enfield
544.	Gypo and Animal
545.	18
546.	Reading
547.	True: ranked no. 23
548.	Fulham

549. Norway

550. Warlock

BIG WINS – 1

551.	v. Tranmere Rovers (Away),	
	December 2005, League	4-1
552.	v. Camberley Town (Home),	
	November 1998, FA Cup, 1st round	5-0
553.	v. Brighton & Hove Albion (Home),	
	September 1991, League Cup, 2nd round, 1st leg	4-1
554.	v. Bristol Rovers (Away),	
	December 1994, League	4-1
555.	v. Oxford United (Home),	
	December 2000, Football League Trophy, 1st round	4-1
556.	v. Exeter City (Home),	
	May 1999, League	3-0
557.	v. Portsmouth (Home),	
	September 1992, League	4-1
558.	v. Walsall (Home),	
	February 2006, League	5-0
559.	v. Bristol City (Home),	
	October 1992, League	5-1
560.	v. Swansea City (Home),	
	May 1999, League	4-1

DAVID McCULLOCH

561. 1911

562. Hamilton

563. Third Lanark

564. Heart of Midlothian

565. £6,000

566. 85

567. 3

568. Falkirk, Brentford, Aldershot, Chelsea, Bournemouth & Boscombe Athletic and Swansea Town

569. Waterford

570. Alloa Athletic

1960s

571.   Johnny Brooks
572.   Billy Gray
573.   1962/1963
574.   16th
575.   Blackpool
576.   Ray Reeves
577.   £12,000
578.   Joe Bonson
579.   14th
580.   36

CAPS FOR MY COUNTRY

581.	Idris Hopkins	12 Wales caps
582.	Bill Slater	12 England caps
583.	David McCulloch	7 Scotland caps
584.	Kenny Sansom	86 England caps
585.	Sam Sodje	2 Nigerian caps
586.	Gerry Peyton	33 Republic of Ireland caps
587.	Alex Graham	1 Scotland cap
588.	Marcus Gayle	14 Jamaican caps
589.	Chris Hughton	53 Republic of Ireland caps
590.	Graham Rix	17 England caps

POT LUCK – 1

591.   Hounslow
592.   12,763
593.   True
594.   Greg Dyke
595.   5th
596.   Buzz Bee
597.   True
598.   One Touch To Go
599.   Queens Park Rangers
600.   True

HOW MUCH DID THEY PAY?

601.   Bill Gorman   £7,000

602.	Gavin Mahon	£50,000
603.	John Salako	Free
604.	Leo Fortune-West	£60,000
605.	Sam Sodje	Free
606.	Andy Sinton	£25,000
607.	Dudley Campbell	Free
608.	Gary Blissett	£60,000
609.	Ian Holloway	£25,000
610.	Danny Cullip	£75,000

GOALSCORERS – 1

611.	Michael Allen	11
612.	Dean Holdsworth	54
613.	Mark Lazarus	20
614.	Paul Abrahams	8
615.	Nigel Gleghorn	1
616.	Marcus Gayle (both spells)	24
617.	Frank Morrad	2
618.	Patsy Hendren	15
619.	Terry Hurlock	18
620.	Earnest Muttitt	25

LLOYD OWUSU

621.	1976
622.	Slough
623.	Slough Town
624.	Ron Noades
625.	76
626.	22
627.	Ghana
628.	Yeovil Town
629.	Rotherham United
630.	True

1950s

631.	1952
632.	Sid Russell
633.	Watford

634. *Tommy Lawton*
635. *Terry Ledgerton*
636. *B.E.M.: British Empire Medal*
637. *Ian Dargie*
638. *Bill Dodgin Snr*
639. *Bobby Fisher*
640. *John Hales*

PAUL EVANS
641. *1974*
642. *Shrewsbury Town*
643. *£110,000*
644. *Preston North End and Burnley*
645. *31*
646. *Midfield*
647. *Bradford City*
648. *2*
649. *Dennis Wise*
650. *True*

ALAN NELMES
651. *Chelsea*
652. *1967*
653. *Jimmy Sirrel*
654. *Players' Player of the Year*
655. *1948*
656. *316*
657. *9*
658. *2*
659. *3*
660. *1976*

CHRIS KAMARA
661. *1957*
662. *Middlesbrough*
663. *Portsmouth*
664. *£50,000*
665. *Stan Bowles*

666.   28
667.   False: he won it in the 1983/1984 season
668.   Bradford City
669.   Stoke City
670.   Frank McLintock

ATTENDANCES

671.	v. Swansea City (Home),	
	May 2006, play-off semi-final, 2nd leg	10,652
672.	v. Crewe Alexandra (Wembley),	
	May 1997, play-off final	34,149
673.	v. Rotherham United (Home),	
	February 1996, League	3,446
674.	v. Sheffield Wednesday (Home),	
	May 2005, play-off semi-final, 2nd leg	10,823
675.	v. Huddersfield (Home),	
	May 1995, play-off semi-final, 2nd leg	11,161
677.	v. Mansfield Town (Home),	
	August 1998, League	4,846
677.	v. Bury (Home),	
	May 2001, League	4,596
678.	v. Blackpool (Home),	
	August 2006, League	6,048
679.	v. Hereford United (Home),	
	April 2008, League	6,246
680.	v. Bournemouth (Home),	
	May 2004, League	9,485

DEAN HOLDSWORTH

681.   1968
682.   Walthamstow
683.   Watford
684.   Steve Perryman
685.   54
686.   Wimbledon
687.   Northern Ireland 'B' (10 May 1994)
688.   Redbridge
689.   Peter Beadle

690. *False: his twin brother's name is David, but the rest of the*
question is correct

BIG WINS – 2

691.	*v. Blackpool (Home),*	
	November 2002, League	**5-0**
692.	*v. Bury (Home),*	
	October 2001, League	**5-1**
693.	*v. Shrewsbury Town (Away),*	
	August 1997, League Cup, 1st round, 2nd leg	**5-3**
694.	*v. Gainsborough Trinity (Home),*	
	November 2003, FA Cup, 1st round	**7-1**
695.	*v. Plymouth Argyle (Away),*	
	August 1994, League	**5-1**
696.	*v. Northampton (Home),*	
	March 2003, League	**3-0**
697.	*v. Plymouth Argyle (Home),*	
	December 1994, League	**7-0**
698.	*v. Tranmere Rovers (Home),*	
	September 2001, League	**4-0**
699.	*v. York City (Home),*	
	April 1995, League	**3-0**
700.	*v. Cambridge United (Home),*	
	January 1995, League	**6-0**

MARCUS GAYLE

701. *1970*
702. *Hammersmith*
703. *Brentford*
704. *24 (1st spell 1989-94, 2nd spell 2005-06)*
705. *Aldershot Town*
706. *He scored his first career hat-trick*
707. *Jermaine Darlington*
708. *Jamaica*
709. *AFC Wimbledon*
710. *True*

TOMMY HIGGINSON

711. 1937
712. 15
713. Kilmarnock
714. Malcolm McDonald
715. True
716. Queens Park Rangers
717. Hillingdon Borough
718. 388
719. Inside forward/wing half
720. Malcolm McDonald, Tommy Cavanagh, Billy Gray, Jimmy Sirrel
       and Frank Blunstone

GARY BLISSETT

721. 1964
722. Manchester
723. Crewe Alexandra
724. £60,000
725. 79
726. Peterborough United
727. Southend United
728. £350,000
729. Singapore (Sembawang Rangers) and Germany (SV Elversberg)
730. Striker

POT LUCK – 2

731. True
732. John Buttigieg
733. Gus Hurdle
734. Marcus Bent
735. Brett Johnson
736. Chic Brodie
737. Northampton Town
738. Goalkeeper
739. £10,000
740. Ibrahima Sonko

POSITIONS IN THE TEAM

741.	John Burns	Inside forward
742.	John Steel	Fullback
743.	Pat Kruse	Centre half
744.	Anthony Harper	Wing half
745.	Richard Parker	Centre forward
746.	James Elliott	Defender
747.	Jack Astley	Right back
748.	William Relph	Winger
749.	Gary Phillips	Goalkeeper
750.	James Lawrence	Midfield

GOALSCORERS – 2

751.	Johnny Brooks	36
752.	John Fielding	18
753.	David Nelson	5
754.	Darren Powell	6
755.	Steve Sidwell	4
756.	Roger Cross (both spells)	54
757.	John Salako	4
758.	Gordon Neilson	15
759.	Neil Smillie (both spells)	18
760.	John O'Mara	28

YEARS AT THE CLUB – 2

761.	William Dobson	1999-2006
762.	Kenneth Horne	1950-61
763.	Thomas Sperrin	1949-56
764.	Edward Ware	1928-33
765.	John Fielding	1963-65
766.	Terry Bullivant	1983-86
767.	Joseph Grozier	1937-49
768.	Jack Holliday	1932-44
769.	Denny Mundee	1993-95
770.	Douglas Allder	1977-80

POT LUCK – 3

771.   Canada

772. 3
773. *Millwall*
774. *£18,000*
775. *Charlie MacDonald*
776. *Midfield (centre)*
777. *1927*
778. *77*
779. *Ricky Shakes*
780. *True*

HARRY CURTIS

781. *Guv'nor*
782. *Gillingham*
783. *5th*
784. *21*
785. *Plymouth Argyle*
786. *Holloway (1890)*
787. *Romford and Walthamstow Grange*
788. *Alf Capper*
789. *718*
790. *True*

GOALSCORERS – 3

791.	*James Bain*	*2*
792.	*Vivian Woodward*	*4*
793.	*Mick Block*	*30*
794.	*Brian Statham*	*1*
795.	*Paul Walker*	*5*
796.	*Stan Bowles*	*16*
797.	*Jay Tabb*	*20*
798.	*Dean Smith*	*16*
799.	*Kevin Rapley*	*12*
800.	*George Francis (both spells)*	*124*

NOTES

NOTES

NOTES

NOTES

NOTES

NOTES

NOTES

NOTES

www.apexpublishing.co.uk